The DeSalle Collection of
Smith-Miller &
Doepke Trucks

by:

Don & Barb DeSalle

© 1997

Published by:

L-W Book Sales

P.O. Box 69
Gas City, IN 46933

ISBN#: 0-89538-093-5

Published by: L-W Book Sales
                P.O. Box 69
                Gas City, IN 46933

Please write for our free catalog.

Printed by: IMAGE GRAPHICS, INC., Paducah, Kentucky

DEDICATION

Thank you to my wife, Barb and my children Dan, Chris and Sonja for all the help and support they have given me over the years.

ABOUT THE AUTHORS

Don and his lovely wife Barb, are nationally known as collectors of toy trucks. Trucks included in this book are part of the DeSalle's collection. With the success of their first book "Collectors Guide to Tonka Trucks", the DeSalle's have once again decided to share another part of their collection, Smith-Miller & Doepke toys. Many years of travel across the U.S. have resulted in a most complete collection in excellent condition. As both collectors and promotors, the DeSalles have an excellent knowledge base for the market trends and values of toys.

Don DeSalle, a native of Toledo, Ohio, graduated from Rogers High School. Don was All State in football, and received a scholarship to play football for Indiana University. Don went on to obtain a B.A. (70) and an M.A. (72) from Indiana University in Geology and Chemistry, and was named an All American football player, playing in the Rose Bowl, the Senior Bowl, and the North and South game. His football career continued as he played briefly with the Buffalo Bills.

Don taught high school science and coached football for several years. His interest in race cars lead to his ownership of Paragon Speedway, a sprint car track, and sponsorship for a sprint car and a Nascar. Currently, Don is one of the largest antique toy show promoters in the United States, promoting shows in Atlanta, Nashville, Louisville, Cincinnati, Dayton, Springfield, Indianapolis and Allentown, PA. He publishes the American Toy Collector, a monthly antique toy truck magazine, and manufactures the DeSalle Collector Truck Line, a limited edition of 300 pressed steel collector trucks.

Barb DeSalle is a native of Daleville, Indiana and obtained a B.A. (71), M.S. (75), M.S. (81), Ed. S. (81) from Ball State University. She has completed the course work on her doctorate and has research on Satellite Communications, at Ball State University. Barb is past president of Anderson University Phi Delta Kappa, and has served as a middle school principal, high school assistant principal, dean of girls, grant proposal development director, and a teacher. Barb and Don are constantly busy with DeSalle Promotions, Inc. promoting antique toy shows across the country.

The DeSalle's have three children, Dan and Chris DeSalle, and Sonja Gentry. Dan and Sonja attend Indiana University, and Chris attends Ball State University. All three help with the toy shows as their schedules allow.

Don DeSalle
5106 Knollwood
Anderson, IN 46011

1-800-392-8697

TABLE OF CONTENTS

PRICING INFORMATION

The values in this book should be used only as a guide. These prices will vary from one section of the country to the other. All prices are also affected by the condition as well as the demand of the piece.

Neither the Author nor the Publisher assumes responsibility for any gains or losses that might be incurred as a result of using this guide.

IDENTIFICATION

Chevy Cab 1946-47

Ford Cab 1945-46

GMC Cab 1948-55

"L" Mack Cab 1950-53

M.I.C. Cab 1953-55

"B" Mack Cab 1954-55

1945-46 Smitty Toys Logo

Door Decal on a Chevy Cab 1946-47

Door Decal on these models:
GMC 1948-55
"L" Mack 1950-53
"B" Mack 1954-55

M.I.C. Door Decal 1953-55

M.I.C. Door Decal 1953-55

Ford & Chevy wheel, hubcap and tire, 1945-47

GMC 1947-48 wheel, hubcap and tire

Chevy wheel, hubcap and tire, 1946-47

GMC wheel and tire, 1954-55

Wheel and tire used on a GMC Searchlight Truck, 1953

Wheel and tire used on an "L" Mack 1950-53

Wheel and tire used on "B" Mack, 1954-55

Wheel and tire used on M.I.C., 1953-55

"L" Mack Frame, 1950-51

"L" Mack Frame, 1952-53

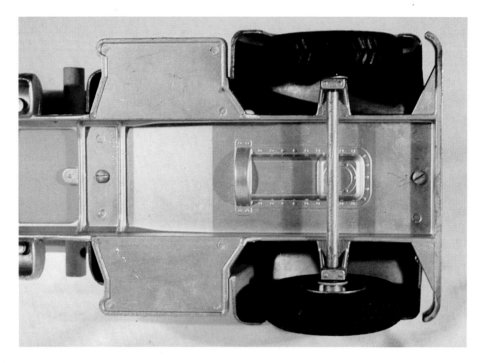

"B" Mack Frame, 1954-55

"L" Mack bumper with no web supports, 1950-51
(*Note: Bull Dog used on early "L" Macks*)

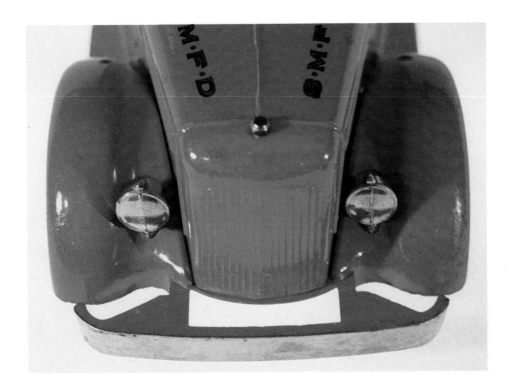

"L" Mack Bumper showing webbed supports

"L" Mack Short Gas Tank, 1952-53

"L" Mack Long Tanks, 1950-51

Latch used on an "L" Mack Tandom Lumber ,
a Mobile Oil Tanker and a Merchandise Van

Hook and latch for the rear of a Tandom Lumber "B" Mack

M.I.C. Truck showing the steering wheel, seat,
opening doors and latches

Box for Cab Over Mobile Tanker, 1949

Box for Drive-O Truck, 1949

Box for Cab Over Dump, 1952

Box for Cab Over Coca Cola, 1954

Box for "L" Mack Materials, 1950

Identification continued . . .

Box for "B" Mack Blue Diamond Dump, 1954

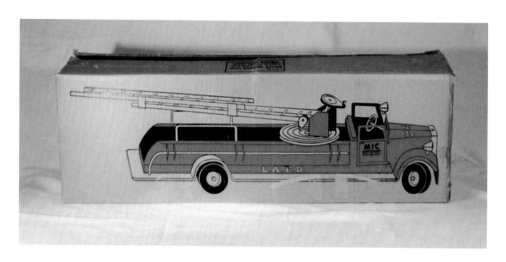

Box for M.I.C. Aerial Ladder

Box for M.I.C. #533 Hydraulic Dump

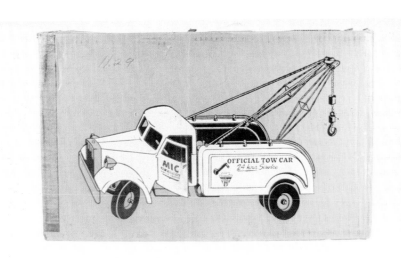

Box for M.I.C. Wrecker, 1953

FORD CABOVERS 1945-46

In 1945 Smith Miller made the first aluminum cast cab. It was a cabover, looking somewhat like the Fords of the early 40's. These cabs were roughly cast very thick and heavy with no headlights and a vertical grill. Decals on the doors had the Smitty Toys logo with the word California under it. Tires were made of solid rubber with no treads and a small plain plated hub cap. There were only three Ford style Smitty Trucks; the Coca Cola truck; the Bekins Semi; and the Utility Truck. There was one private label truck, the Sparketta "UP" Bottling truck. Pictured are two unique examples of this rare Ford private label, one with the Smith logo and the other with a "Lifetime Toy Co., P.O. Box 169, Beverly Hills, Calif." logo. Also worth noting is the Bekins Semi has no rear doors. Early Ford cab Smittys are rare and in any condition, are an excellent addition to your Smith Miller collection.

1946 Smitty Utility Truck

1945 Ford Coca-Cola

1945 Ford Bekins Van

1946 Ford "Sparkeeta Up"
Bottling Truck

1945 Ford "Sparkeeta Up"
Bottling Truck

CHEVY CABOVERS 1946-47

In 1946, Smith Miller introduced another line of cab over trucks, the Chevy cabs. Casting techniques improved and the quality of castings had finer details. Now there were head lights on the fenders and the grill. Bars were more detailed, outlines for the doors and hood vents were included.

The product line increased to nine trucks over the two years of Chevy cabs. #102M Material, #103-L Lumber truck, #104-I Ice truck, #105-M Milk truck, #106 Coca Cola truck, #107-G Grocery truck, #108-V Bekins van, #109-S Stake truck, and the #1 10-L Livestock truck. Logos on the doors had "Smitty Toys" with "S/Miller" on top, and "California" below.

#107-G Chevy
Heinz Grocery Truck, 1947

#205-P Chevy
Triton Oil Truck, late 1947

#105-M Arden Milk 1946

#105-M Chevy
Arden Milk Truck, 1947

The back of the 1946 Arden Milk Truck

Chevy Cabovers 1946-47 continued . . .

#106-C Chevy Coca-Cola, 1946

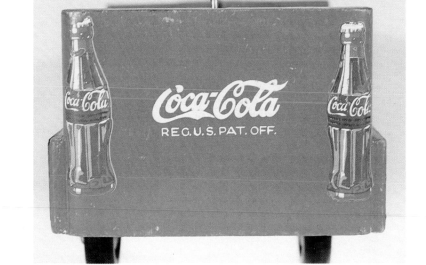

Back view of the Chevy Coca-Cola

#106-C Coca-Cola, 1947

Another variation of a
Chevy Cab Coca-Cola Truck

#102-M Chevy
Material Truck, 1946

#104-I Union Ice Truck
(Ken Gregory Truck)

Chevy Cabovers 1946-47 continued . . .

#110-L Chevy
Livestock Semi, 1946-47
(Ken Gregory Truck)

#109-S Chevy Stake Semi, 1946-47
(Ken Gregory Truck)

#110-L Chevy
Live Stock Semi, 1947
(side racks missing)

An unusual Chevy Cab
Silver Streak, 1947

GMC CABOVERS 1947-55

Smith Miller continued to refine their truck line in 1947 with the introduction of the GMC style cabs. These early trucks had solid rubber tires with straight treads, and large plated hubcaps with S-M stamped in them. Trucks introduced in 1947 were given the #200 number as their series.

Smith Miller offered eleven trucks in their 200 line. They were as follows: #200-L Lumber truck, #202-M Material truck, #203-H Heinz truck, #204-A Arden Milk, #205-P Oil truck, #206-C Coca Cola truck, #208-B Bekins Vanliner, #209-T Timber Giant, #210-S Stake Tractor-Trailer, #211-L Sunkist Tractor Trailer, and the #212-R Silver Streak.

In 1948, Smith Miller changed their logo to emphasize the partnership. Solid rubber tires with straight treads were still used as well as the SM embossed hubcaps. The company produced 12 models for 1948. They were as follows: #301-W Wrecker, #305-T Triton Oil, #306-C Coca Cola, #307-L Logger, #308-V Lyon Van, #309-S Super-Tractor Trailer, #310-H HiWay Freighter, #311-E Silver Streak, and the #312-P P.I.E. Tractor Trailer.

In 1949, the big change was an all new wheel design, an all cast four spoke hub was made with a separate rubber tire. Door logos stayed the same and all trucks manufactured in this year were given 400 catalog numbers.

The 1949 product line from Smith Miller was as follows: #401-W Wrecker, #402-M Material Truck, #403-R Rack Truck, #404-B Bank of America Truck, #405-L Lumber Truck, #407-V Lyon Van Tractor Trailer, #408-H Machinery Hauler, #409-G Mobile Gas Tanker, #410-F Trans Continental, #411-E Silver Streak, #412-P P.I.E., and #4X-0 Drive-O dump.

Smith-Miller continued to make cabover GMC style trucks until 1955. Production was greatly reduced as an all new larger L-Mack series was introduced in 1950. One marked change in the cabover line was in 1954, with the new 5 spoke cash wheels similar to the "B" model trucks introduced that year. Catalog numbers changed in the years as follows: 1950 - #500's, 1951 #600's, 1952 #700's, 1953 #800's, 1954 back to the #400's, 1955 the final year used both #400's and #500's. Most notable trucks manufactured in this period of time were the #420 Coca Cola of #802 Emergency tow truck, the #810 Searchlight Truck both of 1953, the #403 Scoop Dump of 1954, and the #420 Coca-Cola of 1955.

In the following pages are photos of the Smith-Miller caover trucks. Collecting cabover trucks will prove to be very challenging if you try to obtain all the cabovers including the variations. Happy Collecting.

GMC Cab Coca-Cola Truck

Three views:

#420 GMC Coca-Cola Truck, 1955
(note "B" Mack style 5 spoke wheels).

The back view of #420 Coca-Cola Truck

#420 GMC Coca-Cola Truck with Box

#302-M GMC
Materials Truck, 1948

#402-M GMC
Materials Truck, 1949

#203-H GMC
Heinz Grocery Truck, 1948

#403-R GMC
Rack Truck, 1949

#305-T GMC
Triton Oil Truck, 1948

#405-T GMC
Triton Oil Truck, 1949

#4X-O GMC
"Drive-O" Truck, 1949

#504-D GMC Dump Truck, 1950

#704-D GMC Dump Truck
with box, 1952

#403 GMC Scoop Dump, 1954

#301-W GMC Wrecker, 1948

#401-W GMC Wrecker, 1949

#802 GMC
Emergency Tow Truck, 1953

#304-K GMC
Kraft Foods Truck, 1948

Rexall Truck, 1948

#404-B GMC Bank of
America Truck, 1949

#701 GMC
U.S. Treasury Truck, 1952

Rear doors showing lock on the
U.S. Treasury Truck, also on
the Bank America Truck.

#310-H GMC
Hi-way Freighter
Tractor Trailer, 1948

#311-E Silver Streak
Express Tractor Trailer, 1948

#411-E GMC Silver Streak
Tractor Trailer, 1949

#211-L Sunkist
Tractor Trailer, 1947

#806 GMC Silver Streak
Tractor Trailer, 1953

#409-G GMC
Tanker, 1949

Rear view of the Mobilgas Tanker

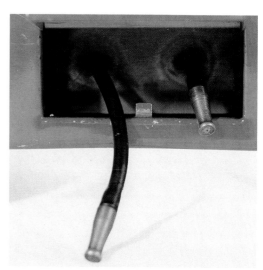

Side view showing the hoses
on #409 Mobilgas Tanker

GMC Eldon Miller
Gas Tanker, 1949
(Rare)

1950 "Co-op" Tanker
(Rare)

Close-up of "Co-op" Tanker decal

Rear view of "Co-op" Tanker

41

#410-F GMC
Transcontinental
Tractor Trailer, 1949

#309-S GMC Super Cargo
Tractor Trailer, 1948

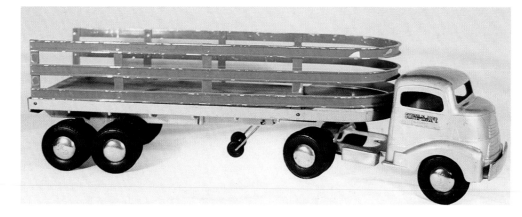

#308-V GMC Lyon Van
Tractor Trailer, 1948

#407-V GMC Lyon Van
Tractor Trailer, 1949

Rear view showing the door on the
Lyon Tractor Trailer

#208-B GMC Bekins
Vanliner, 1947

McCormick Farmall
Tractor Trailer, 1948

Rear view of the
McCormick Farmall Truck

#312-P GMC Pacific
Intermountain Express
Tractor Trailer, 1948

#412-P GMC
Pacific Intermountain Express
Tractor Trailer, 1949

View of the rear doors of the
Pacific Intermountain Express

1949 "B" Mack Semi
(Rare)

Marshall Field & Company
Truck, 1948

#406-L GMC Lumber
Tractor Trailer, 1949

#408-H GMC
Machinery Hauler, 1949

#804 GMC
Machinery Hauler, 1953

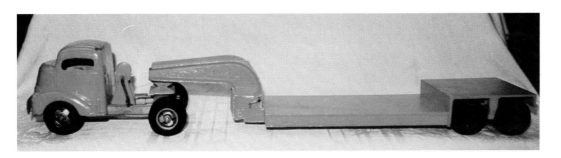

Rogers Lowboy
only 700 made,
(Very Rare)

#810 GMC
Searchlight Truck, 1953

Rear view of the GMC
Searchlight Truck,
NOTE: Used the large L-Mack
Tires on the trailer.

"L" MACKS 1950-1953

Smith Miller introduced five all new trucks for 1950. These trucks were copies of a Mack Truck that graced the American highways since the early 1940's, the famed "LF" Mack truck. Known to collectors as "L" Macks, the first five trucks were the "L" Mack Material truck, the "L" Mack Lyons, the "L" Mack Tandem Timber, the "L" Mack P.I.E., and the "L" Mack Aerial Ladder. Manufactured of cast aluminum, with a separate cab and frame, incorporating cast fender mounted headlights, cast Bulldog (only 1950-51 models) and cast four spoke wheels which were carried over from earlier GMC models. The tires of these trucks carried no logos or company name.

"L" Mack frames contained fuel tanks on both sides. These tanks came in two varieties, "long" and "short". "Long tanks" measuring 2 1/4 inches in length were used only on the early 1950-51 trucks. Later, "short" tank trucks not only incorporated shorter tanks, but also had a detailed oil pan and clutch housing on the underside of the frame, and the Bulldog was replaced with a simple radiator cap.

Early Smith Miller "L" Mack trucks had a real problem with the ends of the bumpers breaking. These bumpers were part of the cast frame and there was no way to replace the broken bumpers. To improve on this problem, Smith Miller reinforced the bumper with a webbing on the later "L" Mack trucks. So, if your "L" Mack truck has no Bulldog, short tanks, and a reinforced bumper, it was probably manufactured in 1952 or 1953.

Wood was an important part of the Smith Miller "L" Mack truck. The incorporation of wood in the form of mahogany or fruit wood was used for two reasons, the ease of construction, and to help keep the prices down on an already pricey "L" Mack truck. (Ladder trucks retailed for $27.95 in 1950!)

Wood was used to form the early tandem timber truck, (in later years it was replaced with aluminum). Material truck used an aluminum trimmed wood bed. Complete beds were made of wood on the Telephone trucks, Army Personnel and Materials trucks. The Mobile Tandem tanker was one of the most dramatic uses of wood by Smith Miller, with its two large tank bodies setting on wood platforms topped by aluminum cat walks. This is a very beautiful truck in its original condition and a prize to any Smith Miller collection.

#706 "L" Mack Material Truck

"L" Mack Orange Materials Truck, 1952. The original truck has load of one large crate and one small crate, three barrels and two boards.

"L" Mack
Army Personnel Carrier, 1952

#606 "L" Mack
Army Materials Truck, 1952

"L" Mack
International
Paper Co., 1952

"L" Mack
Mobilgas Tanker, 1952

Rear view of the
"L" Mack Mobilgas

"L" Mack Mobilgas Tandem Tanker, 1952

"L" Mack
Aerial Ladder, 1950
*(Note: Double extension
ground ladders)*

"L" Mack Aerial Ladder
brass end crank handles, 1950

"L" Mack
Aerial Ladder, 1953
*(Note: Ladder
platform in red)*

"L" Mack Bell Telephone Truck,
olive green color

"L" Mack Bell Telephone Truck, 1952

"L" Mack Tandem
Timber Truck, 1950

Pup Trailer for
Tandem Timber Truck

"L" Mack Tandem
Timber Truck

"L" Mack
Tamdem Timber, 1952

"L" Mack Lyon Van, 1950

"L" Mack Sibleys
1950, (Very Rare)

"L" Mack Merchandise Van, 1951

"L" Mack Merchandise Van and Trailer, 1951

"L" Mack West Coast Transport, 1952

Rear view of the West Coast Transport
showing the doors

#709 "L" Mack
Blue Diamond Dump
Truck, 1952

#709 "L" Mack
Blue Diamond Dump Truck
with original box

"L" Mack
Orange Hydraulic
Dump (Rare)

L Macks 1950-53 continued . . .

"L" Mack Bekins
Van, large decal, 1952

"L" Mack Bekins
Van, small decal
variation, 1953

Rear view of the "L" Mack
Bekins Van, showing the door

"L" Mack P.I.E., 1950

"L" Mack
Country Garden, 1950
(Very Rare)

Rear view of the
"L" Mack Country Garden

A close up view of the Country Garden decal

M.I.C.
1953-54-55

Smith Miller introduced a new truck line in 1953, the M.I.C. which stands for the Miller-Ironson Corporation. The company changed its name and door decals with the new M.I.C. These trucks had opening doors with working handles, seats, floor boards, and a steering wheel that actually worked to steer the truck. The trucks only weakness was the door hinges, and opening the doors to steer the truck without using caution resulted in broken hinges. Thus, its not uncommon to find M.I.C. trucks with broken doors or no doors at all! There were changes made in the hinges, the upper hinge was higher on some trucks.

Wheels and tires were also all new for the M.I.C. Wheels were cast aluminum that were very realistic and had no openings as found on "1" Mack wheels. Tires were unique to the M.I.C. with a straight tread and lugs around the side walls with no logos. Collectors have noted they have original M.I.C. trucks with "B" Mack style wheels and tires, and "B" Mack trucks with M.I.C. style wheels and tires. It was obvious that Smith Miller used whatever product available to complete trucks in the later years.

M.I.C. trucks are not an exact replica of real life trucks such as the "L" Macks and the "B" Macks of their day. Many collectors think it resembles an auto car and looking at the grill and radiator shell, it does indeed look like an early 50's auto car.

The most unique product of the M.I.C. line was not a truck at all, it was the Lincoln and House Trailer. Marketed in 1953, this car-trailer combination, took advantage of the "I Love Lucy", a famous series using a Lincoln and house trailer.

The trailer had a blue steel roof and polished aluminum sides, cast doors and window frames, and the inside had simulated furniture. The car came in two tone blue and cream, and was cast in aluminum and had a steering wheel that actually worked.

Finding this set in original condition will be difficult as they were not plentiful to start with, and often got separated in later years.

M.I.C. Lumber Truck

#532 M.I.C. Lift-O-Matic

Rear view of #532
M.I.C. Lift Gate in lowered position

M.I.C. Tow Truck

M.I.C. Tow Truck
with polished sides

Rear view of the M.I.C. Tow Truck

M.I.C. Aerial Ladder Truck

M.I.C. Aerial Ladder, 1954
(Note: "B" Mack Wheels)

M.I.C. Tractor and P.I.E. Trailer, 1954
(Ken Gregory Truck)

#533 M.I.C. Hydraulic
Dump Truck

#533 M.I.C. Hydraulic
Dump Truck with original box

Smith Miller
Freight Car Toy Chest

M.I.C. Tractor Trailer

M.I.C. Roadstar
Tractor Trailer

M.I.C. Teamsters
Tractor Trailer

Rear view of the M.I.C. Trailer showing the doors

M.I.C. Lincoln Capri

M.I.C. House Trailer

"B" MACKS

    Smith Miller introduced another new truck in 1954, the "B" Mack. This was an exact replica of Mack Truck's new "B" model Mack, which hit the highways in 1953. The Smith Miller logo of the earlier trucks was once again back on the doors of this new toy. Smith Miller even embossed the name on the sidewalls of its tires. Even the wheels were new in style, cast in aluminum with five spokes. Added to the cab roof was a cast air horn and cast running lights on each side. Headlights were also cast in aluminum as well as the radiator emblem.

    Frames were cast in one piece aluminum, as well as a very detailed cast cab with excellent detail right down to the Mack Bulldog embossed on the sides of the hood.

    Smith Miller only made seven "B" Mack style of trucks. They were as follows: #404 the "B" Mack Lumber Truck, #405 "B" Mack Silver Streak, #406 "B" Mack Bekins, #407 "B" Mack Search Light, #409 "B" Mack P.I.E., and the #410 "B" Mack Aerial Ladder. There is one unique "B" Mack Smith Miller, the "B" Mack Jr. Aerial Ladder. This truck featured an open cab with a cast windshield, and a cast grill and bumper combination. A cranking mechanism similar to the M.I.C. Aerial Ladder was used to raise the ladders. A red flasher was mounted on the hood and had a battery to light the light as the wheels were turned. This could have been a prototype of what was to come before Smith Miller closed its doors in 1955.

#405 "B" Mack
Silver Streak

#406 "B" Mack Bekins Van

#408 "B" Blue Diamond
Dump Truck

Rear view of the "B" Mack
Blue Diamond Dump Truck

#408 "B" Mack
Blue Diamond Dump Truck,
with original box

"B" Macks continued . . .

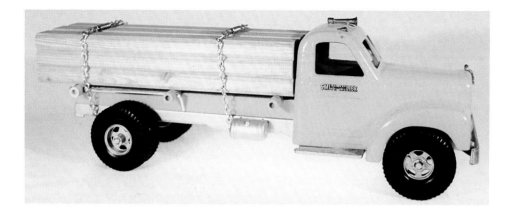

#404 "B" Mack Lumber Truck

#404 "B" Mack
Lumber Truck
with Pup

#410 "B" Mack
Aerial Ladder Truck

#409 "B" Mack Pacific
Intermountain Express, also
made with 10 wheel tractor

#407 "B" Mack Searchlight

Rear view of the "B" Mack Searchlight

"B" Mack
Watson Brothers
(Very Rare)

DOEPKE

Doepke or "Model Toys" was one of the finest manufacturers of toys in America. Founders, Charles Doepke and his brother Fred Doepke, started business in a B & O Railroad building in Oakley, Ohio. The company's full title was the "Charles Wm. Doephe Mfg. Co., Inc.". In the beginning, the two brothers started in the machine tool business. After WWII, they entered the toy business. The very first toy was the Wooldridge. In 1950 they moved to a new production plant in Rossmoyne, Ohio. Capable of manufacturing more than 200,000 toys a year. Made of superior quality and authentic in every way to their real life counterparts, Doepke Toys had several variations in their basic construction as manufacturing continued. These changes were usually to eliminate more intricate operational procedures such as changes in pulleys, gears, or crank handles. One production change of note was on the D-6 Caterpillar dozer. The early models 1952, had front axles held tightly forward by springs to help absorb shock and protect the tract. Later models eliminated the springs and used axles like the rear axles.

In 1955, Doepke started a line of backyard riding toys. The #2021 Yardbird, was a chain driven hand car and a flat bed car. Designed to ride on tracks 71/2 inches wide, there was a complete array of straight tracks, curved tracks, warning lights, cross bars and switches to buy as accessories. There was also a Super Yardbird, a motorized unit resembling a diesel engine. Some were powered by a 6 volt battery and others with a gas powered four cycle engine. In the final years, Doepke made a complete line of wooden toys.

Doepke Toys were ultimately doomed by competition from lower priced, lighter constructed toys, by manufacturers such as Buddy L, Structo, Nylint, and Tonka. The Charles Wm. Doepke Co., closed the doors of their Rossmoyne plant in 1959.

#2000 "WOOLDRIDGE" EARTH HAULER

Referred to by collectors as the "Wooldridge" this was the first toy that the Doepke Co. produced in 1946. The "Wooldridge" logo is located on the front bumper, the "Model Toys" decals were on the trailer sides. This toy measures 25 inches long and weighs 10 1/2 pounds. The steering control on the early Earth Haulers had a "T" and later an "L" shape. The long bottom doors on the trailer open with gravity, a wire handle is used to release the steel latch, and the doors swing open and the load of dirt falls through by gravity. This great toy was made from 1946-1949 and is difficult to find in excellent condition.

#2001 BUCKET LOADER ("BARBER-GREENE") SWIVEL CHUTE

This great toy was also introduced in 1946 and made through 1950. Called the "Barber-Greene" by collectors, this was a unique toy. A wheel attached to nylon cords turned the chute. The toy was designed so that the bucket conveyor and auger operated together by turning the crank handle. The #2001 bucket loader is 18" high and weighs 10 pounds.

In 1948 the swivel chute was replaced with a fixed chute. Doepke also changed the drive chain design and the hand crank mechanism was moved to the right side. Later 1950 versions were painted orange as pictured.

#2002 CONCRETE MIXER

Introduced in 1947 and made through 1949, the concrete mixer is one of the finest pressed steel examples made of a Jaeger Mixer. It weighs 7 pounds and is 15 inches in length. The tires are Goodyears made of rubber. The mixer drum is painted black and turned by cranking the handle which rotates a chain that fits snugly around the mixer drum. A rubber hose runs down from the water tank sitting on the top of the toy. This is another hard Doepke toy to find in the complete and excellent condition.

#2006 ROAD GRADER

Doepke introduced the Adams Grader in 1948 and made it through 1956. Variations of the grader were different colors and different tires were used, both Goodyear and Firestone tires were used. Measuring 26 inches and weighing 14 pounds, this was a very big toy. Because it was made for 9 years and is very durable, the Adams Grader is one of the more common Doepke Toys.

#2006 ADAMS ROAD GRADER

#2007 UNIT CRANE

This construction toy was introduced by Doepke in 1949 and made through 1954. The outriggers on the toy are functional. This toy is a very realistic copy of the Unit Crane Model 357.

#2008 AERIAL LADDER

Introduced in 1950, and made through 1952, Doepke made an excellent example of the American LaFrance Aerial Ladder. Weighing 11 pounds and measuring 18 inches long, with functional steering and a keywind siren, this toy had play value. Each truck had two 18" aluminum scaling ladders to compliment the large sliding ladders.

Early versions of the #2008 Aerial ladder had a plastic windshield, and some were made without the sirens, and had a battery box and flashing lights. You could also send away for a Doepke Firechief Badge. These badges are rare, and an excellent addition to your Doepke collection.

#2009 EUCLID TRUCK (front view)

#2009 EUCLID TRUCK WITH BOX

Doepke introduced the Euclid in 1950 and manufactured it through 1955. The truck weighed 11 pounds and was 27 inches long. The tractor was detachable and steerable. The bottom doors are released with a rod handle and gravity opens them.

#2009 EUCLID TRUCK

Doepke introduced the Euclid in 1950 and manufactured it through 1956. The truck weighed 11 pounds and was 27 inches long. The tractor was detachable from the trailer and steerable. The bottom doors are released with a rod handle with gravity opening the doors. Early models were orange, others were in green and olive green.

AN EARLY 1950 ORANGE EUCLID WITH BOX

#2010 PUMPER

The Doepke Pumper was introduced in 1952 and made through 1956. The truck was 19 inches long and weighed 8 pounds and fully steerable. The right side of the truck carried a plastic suction hose and on the left side was an 8 3/4 inch aluminum ladder and in the rear were fire extinguishers and a red rubber hose on a reel. The center of the truck has a water tank with a removable lid. Located on the right side of the tank is a pump. Doepke made an authentic replica of an American LaFrance Pumper to take advantage of the huge success of the earlier #2008 Aerial ladder. An excellent complete example will be hard to find.

#2011 HEILINER SCRAPER

#2011 HEILINER SCRAPER WITH BOX

Doepke introduced the #2011 Heiliner in 1951 and made it through 1956. A huge toy weighing 14 pounds and 29 inches long, this is a prized addition to any construction toy collector. The front wheel hub caps have the name "Heil" stamped in them. Its very hard to find this toy in excellent condition.

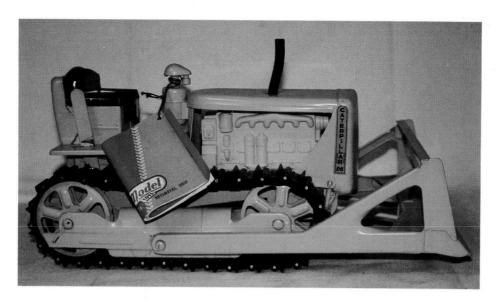

#2012 BULLDOZER

Introduced in 1952 and made through 1956, Doepke made an excellent example of the D-6 Dozer by Caterpillar. Weighing 7 pounds and 15 inches long, the #2012 Bulldozer is a prize to any collector. The engine is made of yellow plastic. It has a rubber smoke stack and a cast aluminum air cleaner. These Bulldozers received many hours of play time and finding an excellent one will be tough.

#2012 BULLDOZER WITH BOX

#2013 BACK LOADER

Doepke introduced this rubber tired version of the Bucket Loader in 1953 through 1956. The auger is used to guide the bucket conveyor which drops it into a delivery chute, which in turn drops material to a conveyor belt, all made possible by cranking a simple handle. This is a massive well built toy and I still have fond memories getting mine for Christmas in 1954!!

#2013 BACK LOADER WITH BOX

#2014 AERIAL LADDER (improved)

Introduced in 1953 and offered through 1956, this was Doepke's finest fire piece. Realism was what Doepke wanted and achieved with this aerial ladder truck. It had cast aluminum ladders with real rungs, 2 - 18 inch scaling ladders, aluminum running boards, outriggers to give stability, and functional steering. This is a great fire toy and many were manufactured, but finding a mint example will still be tough.

#2015 AIRPORT TRACTOR AND TRAILER

Doepke made this set in 1954 through 1956. The tractor was made of a cast alloy and the steering wheel was non functional, molded in the front was the word "CLARK". Trailers were made of stamped steel and one had a removable aluminum panel. Collectors have said there is also a variation made with the "AA" American Airlines logo.

#2015 AIRPORT TRACTOR
(front view)

#2023 SEARCH LIGHT TRUCK

In 1955 Doepke revamped the #2010 Pumper and removed the water reservoir and added a battery box and search light and painted it white. This was a limited run toy. It is highly prized by all collectors and commands high prices in excellent complete condition.

A GROUP OF WOODEN DOEPKE TOYS AND THEIR BOXES

#2017 MT Auto

#2018 Jaguar

PRICE GUIDE

The current prices in this book should be used only as a guide. They are not to set prices, which vary from one section of the country to another. Dealer prices vary greatly and are affected by condition as well as demand. Neither the Author nor the Publisher assumes responsibility for any losses or gains that might be incurred as a result of consulting this guide.

	GOOD	EXCELLENT	MINT
PAGE 24			
Top:	$250	400	575
Bottom:	350	600	1150
PAGE 25			
Top:	$400	700	1100
Middle:	400	700	1100
Bottom:	400	700	1100
PAGE 26			
Top:	$350	600	900
Bottom:	300	500	750
PAGE 27			
Top:	$400	650	1000
Middle:	400	650	1000
PAGE 28			
Top:	$400	700	1400
Bottom:	400	700	1400
PAGE 29			
Top:	$400	650	1100
Middle:	400	650	1100
Bottom:	400	650	1100
PAGE 30			
Top:	$300	600	900
Middle Right:	300	600	900
Middle Left:	300	600	900
Bottom:	300	600	900
PAGE 31			
Bottom:	$500	750	1250
PAGE 32			
Top:	$650	950	1800
Bottom:	___	___	3000
PAGE 33			
Top:	$300	450	650
Middle:	300	500	700
Bottom:	350	600	900

	GOOD	EXCELLENT	MINT
PAGE 34			
Top:	$ 300	450	650
Middle:	250	375	575
Bottom:	250	375	575
PAGE 35			
Top:	$ 350	600	900
Middle:	250	400	650
Bottom:	___	___	950
PAGE 36			
Top:	$1000	1600	2500
Middle:	250	400	650
Bottom:	250	400	650
PAGE 37			
Top:	$ 500	800	1200
Middle:	400	700	1100
Bottom:	600	900	1600
PAGE 38			
Top:	$ 300	450	650
Middle:	450	700	1100
PAGE 39			
Top:	$ 350	550	750
Middle Left:	350	550	750
Middle Right:	350	550	750
Bottom:	350	550	750
PAGE 40			
Top:	$ 350	550	850
Middle:	400	700	1000
PAGE 41			
Top:	$ 800	1350	2100
Middle Left:	900	1500	2500
PAGE 42			
Top:	$ 400	600	850
Middle:	400	600	850
Bottom:	400	600	900

	GOOD	EXCELLENT	MINT			GOOD	EXCELLENT	MINT
PAGE 43					**PAGE 55**			
Top:	$ 450	650	950		Top:	$ 700	1200	1800
Bottom:	400	600	900		Bottom:	950	1550	2800
PAGE 44					**PAGE 56**			
Top:	$ 550	850	1600		Top:	$ 750	1100	1900
Bottom:	350	500	750					
					PAGE 57			
PAGE 45					Top:	$ 750	1200	2200
Top:	$ 350	500	750		Middle:	____	____	3200
Bottom:	550	900	1500		Bottom:	850	1450	2800
PAGE 46					**PAGE 58**			
Top:	$ 450	850	1600		Top:	$ 850	1600	2600
Middle:	350	650	950		Middle:	850	1600	2600
Bottom:	350	650	950					
					PAGE 59			
PAGE 47					Top:	$ 500	700	1100
Top:	$ 550	850	1200		Middle:	750	1200	2800
Middle Left:	1100	2500	3800					
Middle Right:	550	900	1800		**PAGE 60**			
Bottom:	250	450	750		Bottom:	$ 500	750	1200
PAGE 48					**PAGE 61**			
Top:	$ 500	850	1400		Top:	$ 500	750	1200
Bottom:	550	1000	2000		Bottom:	550	775	1300
PAGE 49					**PAGE 62**			
Top:	$ 500	800	1400		Top:	$ 600	800	1400
Middle:	500	800	1400		Bottom:	550	775	1200
Bottom:	750	1150	2000					
					PAGE 63			
PAGE 50					Top:	$ 550	775	1200
Top:	$ 500	800	1300		Bottom:	500	700	1100
Bottom:	700	1400	2500					
					PAGE 64			
PAGE 51					Top:	$ 600	900	1800
Top:	550	750	1200		Bottom:	____	____	2200
Bottom:	550	750	1200					
					PAGE 65			
PAGE 52					Top:	$ 500	800	1200
Top:	$ 900	1500	2100		Middle:	500	800	1000
Bottom:	900	1500	2100		Bottom:	550	850	1400
PAGE 53					**PAGE 66**			
Top:	$ 400	600	900		Top:	$ 650	950	1650
Middle:	100	250	400					
Bottom:	600	800	1400		**PAGE 67**			
					Top:	$ 450	650	950
PAGE 54					Bottom:	300	450	700
Top:	$ 600	800	1400					
Middle:	700	1100	1800					
Bottom:	1200	2200	3800					

	GOOD	EXCELLENT	MINT
PAGE 68			
Top:	$ 450	650	1200
Bottom:	800	1800	2800
PAGE 69			
Top:	$ 850	1450	2800
Bottom:	____	____	3500
PAGE 70			
Top:	$ 500	750	1100
Middle Right:	650	900	1400
Middle Left:	600	850	1400
Bottom:	500	750	1100
PAGE 71			
Top:	900	1800	2800
Bottom:	900	1800	3200
PAGE 72			
Bottom:	$ 300	450	750
PAGE 73			
Top:	$ 350	500	775
Bottom:	300	450	700
PAGE 74			
Top:	$ 300	475	700
PAGE 75			
Top:	$ 250	375	650
Bottom:	250	375	650
PAGE 76			
Top:	$ 350	475	700
Bottom:	200	400	600

	GOOD	EXCELLENT	MINT
PAGE 77			
Bottom:	$ 250	450	650
PAGE 78			
Top:	$ 250	450	650
Bottom:	____	____	1000
PAGE 79			
Top:	$ 200	475	700
Middle:	350	475	800
Bottom:	____	____	1200
PAGE 80			
Top:	$ 300	650	1000
Bottom:	____	____	1500
PAGE 81			
Top:	$ 300	450	700
Bottom:	____	____	1100
PAGE 82			
Top:	$ 300	450	700
Middle:	350	550	850
Bottom:	150	250	350
PAGE 83			
Top:	$ 700	1000	1800
PAGE 85			
Top:	$ 200	450	700
Bottom:	350	650	900